NEW PIANO SERIES

STUDIES ALBUM 5 & 6

ISBN 0-88797-436-8

FREDERICK
HARRIS
MUSIC

Official Examination Studies of The Royal Conservatory of Music - Grades 5 & 6
Études officielles des examens du Royal Conservatory of Music - Niveaux 5 & 6

NEW PIANO SERIES

The *New Piano Series* is designed to serve the needs of teachers and students, as well as those who play the piano solely for their own enjoyment. Each volume of repertoire comprises a carefully selected and edited grouping of pieces from the Baroque, Classical, Romantic, and 20th-century style periods. Studies Albums present compositions especially suited for building technique as well as musicality. Student Guides and recordings are available to assist in the study and enjoyment of the music.

A Note on Editing

Most Baroque and early Classical composers wrote few dynamics, articulation, or other performance indications in their scores. Interpretation was left up to the performer, with the expectation that the performance practice was understood. In this edition, therefore, most of the dynamics and tempo indications in the Baroque and early Classical pieces have been added by the editors. These editorial markings, including fingering and the execution of ornaments, are intended to be helpful rather than definitive. By the late 18th century, composers for the piano included more performance indications in their scores, a trend which became standard in the 19th century. Therefore, in late Classical and Romantic compositions, as well as in the music of our own time, the performer is able to rely on the composers' own markings to a greater extent.

A Note on Performance Practice

The keyboard instruments of the 17th and early to mid-18th centuries lacked the sustaining power of the modern piano. Consequently, the usual keyboard touch was detached rather than legato. The pianist should assume that a lightly articulated touch is appropriate for the Baroque and early Classical music, unless a different approach is indicated either in the music or in a footnote. Slurs are used to indicate legato notes or short phrases.

Piano Syllabus – RCM Examinations

The Royal Conservatory of Music Piano Syllabus gives full details regarding examinations. Teachers, students, and parents are urged to consult the most recent Syllabus for current examination requirements and procedures.

Le "New Piano Series" a été conçu non seulement pour les professeurs et leurs élèves mais aussi ceux qui jouent du piano pour leur propre plaisir. Chaque album inclus un groupe de pièces de style baroque, classique, romantique et 20ème siècle, soigneusement choisies et editées. Les albums d'étude offrent des compositions particulièrement aptes à développer la technique aussi bien que la musicalité. Les guides d'étude et les enregistrements sont disponibles afin d'aider à l'étude des pièces et pour maximiser le plaisir de les jouer.

Note au sujet de l'édition

La plupart des compositeurs baroques et classiques ne notaient ni nuances ni articulations dans leurs partitions. L'interprète était libre de jouer comme il l'entendait en basant bien sûr son interprétation sur la norme de son époque. Dans cette édition, la majeure partie des nuances et articulations trouvées dans les pièces baroques et classiques ont été ajoutées par les éditeurs. Ces additions, incluant doigtés et ornementation, sont fournies à titre indicatif seulement. A partir de la fin du 18ème siècle, les compositeurs commencèrent à inclure de plus en plus d'indications dans leurs partitions. L'interprète de musique de la fin du classique jusqu'à celles de nos jours peut donc beaucoup plus faire appel aux indications du compositeur.

Note au sujet de l'exécution

Les claviers du 17ème et début du 18ème siècles n'avaient pas le ton soutenu d'un piano moderne. Conséquemment l'articulation était surtout détaché plutôt que legato. Le pianiste devrait donc approcher la musique baroque et début du classique avec une légère articulation à moins qu'une approche différente ne soit indiquée dans la partition ou par une note de l'éditeur. Le legato et de courtes phrases sont indiqués par des liaisons.

Piano Syllabus – Examens du RCM

Le Piano Syllabus du Royal Conservatory of Music contient tous les détails au sujet des examens. Il est impératif pour les professeurs, élèves, et parents de consulter le plus récent Syllabus pour être au courant des pré-requis et des règles des examens.

Studies Album 5 & 6
TABLE OF CONTENTS

Grade 5

4	**Study No. 1 / Étude n° 1**	Novelette, Op. 39, No. 22	Dmitri Kabalevsky
5	**Study No. 2 / Étude n° 2**	Allegro in C Major / Allegro en do majeur	Johann Christoph Friedrich Bach
6	**Study No. 3 / Étude n° 3**	Harmony of the Angels / L'harmonie des anges, Op. 100, No. 21	Johann Friedrich Burgmüller
8	**Study No. 4 / Étude n° 4**	Op. 37, No. 27	Antoine Henry Lemoine
9	**Study No. 5 / Étude n° 5**	Op. 65, No. 18	Albert Loeschhorn
10	**Study No. 6 / Étude n° 6**	In the Train / Dans le train	István Szelényi
11	**Study No. 7 / Étude n° 7**	Ave Maria, Op. 100, No. 19	Johann Friedrich Burgmüller
12	**Study No. 8 / Étude n° 8**	Tag / Jeu de poursuite	Ruth Watson Henderson*
13	**Study No. 9 / Étude n° 9**	Op. 125, No. 12	Stephen Heller
14	**Study No. 10 / Étude n° 10**	In the Forest / Dans la forêt, Op. 51, No. 4	Vladimir Ivanovich Rebikov
15	**Study No. 11 / Étude n° 11**	Solfeggio in G Major / Solfège en sol majeur	Johann Christoph Friedrich Bach
16	**Study No. 12 / Étude n° 12**	A Passing Thought / Pensée passagère, Op. 4, No. 1	Samuil Maikapar
17	**Study No. 13 / Étude n° 13**	Tender Flower / Tendre fleur, Op. 100, No. 10	Johann Friedrich Burgmüller
18	**Study No. 14 / Étude n° 14**	Study for the Left Hand / Étude pour la main gauche	Béla Bartók
20	**Study No. 15 / Étude n° 15**	Jumping Jack / Pantin, Op. 11, No. 4	Carl Nielsen
22	**Study No. 16 / Étude n° 16**	Study / Étude	Marko Tajčević

Grade 6

23	**Study No. 1 / Étude n° 1**	Game of Patience / Jeu de réussite, Op. 25, No. 2	Génari Karganov
24	**Study No. 2 / Étude n° 2**	Op. 65, No. 13	Albert Loeschhorn
25	**Study No. 3 / Étude n° 3**	Op. 55, No. 21	Theodor Fürchtegott Kirchner
26	**Study No. 4 / Étude n° 4**	Solfeggio in D Major / Solfège en ré majeur	Johann Christoph Friedrich Bach
27	**Study No. 5 / Étude n° 5**	Heartache / Coeur gros, Op. 32, No. 2	Robert Fuchs
28	**Study No. 6 / Étude n° 6**	Farewell / L'adieu, Op. 100, No. 12	Johann Friedrich Burgmüller
30	**Study No. 7 / Étude n° 7**	Op. 125, No. 10	Stephen Heller
32	**Study No. 8 / Étude n° 8**	Saraband / Sarabande	John Alcock
33	**Study No. 9 / Étude n° 9**	Miniature, Op. 62, No. 6	Theodor Fürchtegott Kirchner
34	**Study No. 10 / Étude n° 10**	Horse Ride / Promenade à cheval	Talivaldis Kenins*
36	**Study No. 11 / Étude n° 11**	A Little Song / Une petite chanson, Op. 47, No. 4	Robert Fuchs
38	**Study No. 12 / Étude n° 12**	Study / Étude	Pál Kadosa
39	**Study No. 13 / Étude n° 13**	Study / Étude	Pál Kadosa
40	**Study No. 14 / Étude n° 14**	Little Willy and the Wind / Petit Willi et le vent, Op. 46, No. 8	Walter Niemann

* Canadian composer / Compositeur canadien

STUDY NO. 1 / ÉTUDE N° 1
Novelette, Op. 39, No. 22

GRADE 5

Dmitri Kabalevsky
(1904 - 1987)

Source: *Twenty-four Pieces for Children,* Op. 39 / *Vingt-quatre pièces pour enfants,* op. 39 (1943)

STUDY NO. 2 / ÉTUDE Nº 2
Allegro in C Major / Allegro en do majeur

GRADE 5

Johann Christoph Friedrich Bach
(1732 - 1795)

All dynamics are editorial. / Toutes les indications des nuances sont de la part des rédacteurs.
Source: *Musikalische Nebenstunden* (1787 - 1788)

STUDY NO. 3 / ÉTUDE N° 3
Harmony of the Angels / L'harmonie des anges
Op. 100, No. 21

GRADE 5

Johann Friedrich Burgmüller
(1806 - 1874)

Allegro moderato ♩ = 108 - 126

Source: *25 Études faciles et progressives*, op. 100 / *25 Easy Progressive Studies*, Op. 100

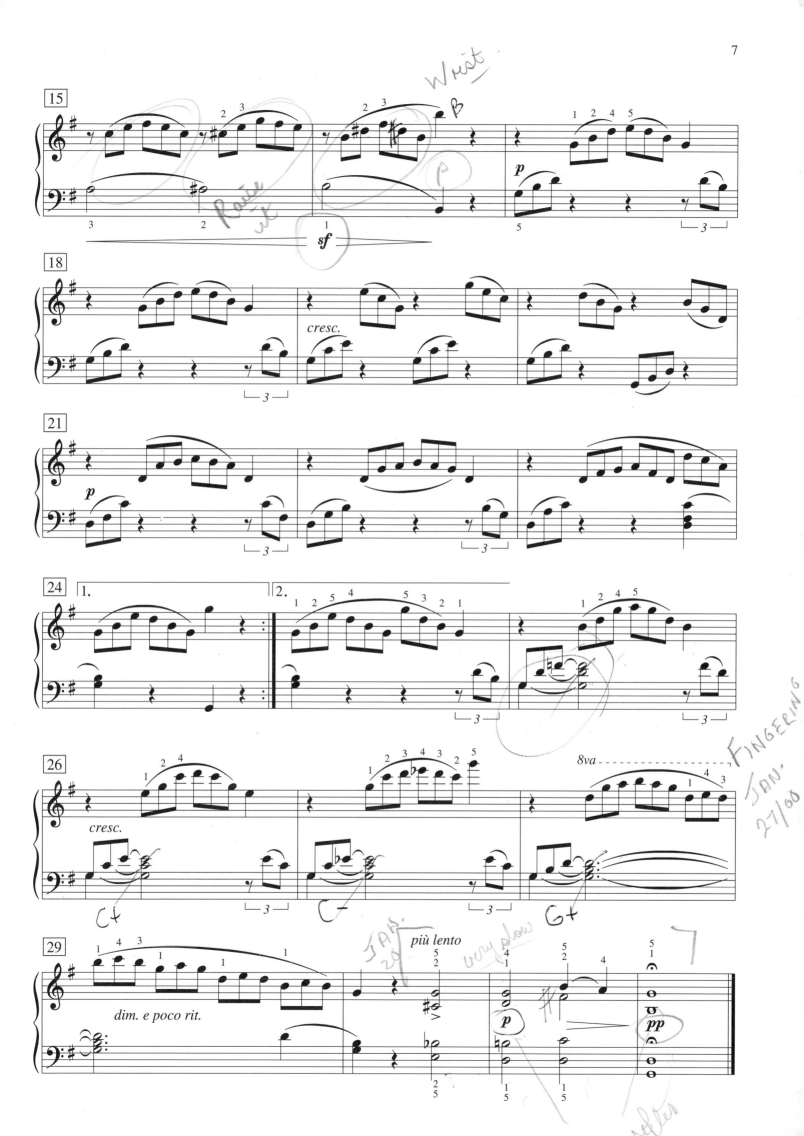

STUDY NO. 4 / ÉTUDE Nº 4
Op. 37, No. 27

GRADE 5

Antoine Henry Lemoine
(1786 - 1854)

Allegretto ♩ = 84 - 96

Source: *Études enfantines,* op. 37 (1841)

STUDY NO. 5 / ÉTUDE N° 5
Op. 65, No. 18

GRADE 5

Albert Loeschhorn
(1819 - 1905)

Andante cantabile ♩ = 96 - 108

Source: *Etüden für Anfänger*, Op. 65

STUDY NO. 6 / ÉTUDE N° 6
In the Train / Dans le train

GRADE 5

István Szelényi
(1904 - 1972)

Allegro di molto ♩ = 152 - 168

Source: *Musical Picture Book / Livre d'images musicales*

STUDY NO. 7 / ÉTUDE Nº 7
Ave Maria, Op. 100, No. 19

GRADE 5

Johann Friedrich Burgmüller
(1806 - 1874)

Source: *25 Études faciles et progressives*, op. 100 / *25 Easy Progressive Studies,* Op. 100

STUDY NO. 8 / ÉTUDE N° 8

Tag / Jeu de poursuite

GRADE 5

Ruth Watson Henderson
(1932 -   )

Crisply / D'un ton acerbe (♩ ♩. = 66 - 72)

Source: *Six Miniatures for Piano*

STUDY NO. 9 / ÉTUDE Nº 9
Op. 125, No. 12

GRADE 5

Stephen Heller
(1813 - 1888)

Moderato preciso ♩ = 84 - 96

Source: *24 Études d'expression et de rythme*, op. 125 / *24 Studies for Expression and Rhythm*, Op. 125

STUDY NO. 10 / ÉTUDE N° 10
In the Forest / Dans la forêt, Op. 51, No. 4

GRADE 5

Vladimir Ivanovich Rebikov
(1866 - 1920)

STUDY NO. 11 / ÉTUDE N° 11
Solfeggio in G Major / Solfège en sol majeur

GRADE 5

Johann Christoph Friedrich Bach
(1732 - 1795)

All dynamics are editorial. / Toutes les indications des nuances sont de la part des rédacteurs.
Source: *Musikalische Nebenstunden* (1787 - 1788)

STUDY NO. 12 / ÉTUDE N° 12
A Passing Thought / Pensée passagère
Op. 4, No. 1

GRADE 5

Samuil Maikapar
(1867 - 1938)

Source: *Huit miniatures*, op. 4 / *Eight Miniatures*, Op. 4

STUDY NO. 13 / ÉTUDE N° 13
Tender Flower / Tendre fleur, Op. 100, No. 10

GRADE 5

Johann Friedrich Burgmüller
(1806 - 1874)

Source: *25 Études faciles et progressives,* op. 100 / *25 Easy Progressive Studies,* Op. 100

STUDY NO. 14 / ÉTUDE Nº 14
Study for the Left Hand / Étude pour la main gauche

GRADE 5

Béla Bartók
(1881 - 1945)

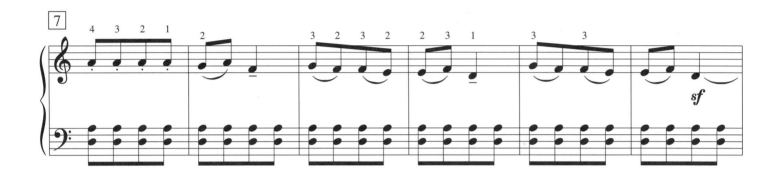

Source: *For Children,* Vol. 1, No. 6 / *Pour les enfants,* vol. 1, nº 6

19

STUDY NO. 15 / ÉTUDE Nº 15
Jumping Jack / Pantin
Op. 11, No. 4

GRADE 5

Carl Nielsen
(1865 - 1931)

Poco Allegretto ♩ = 84 - 96

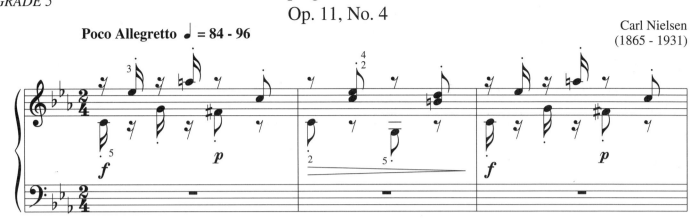

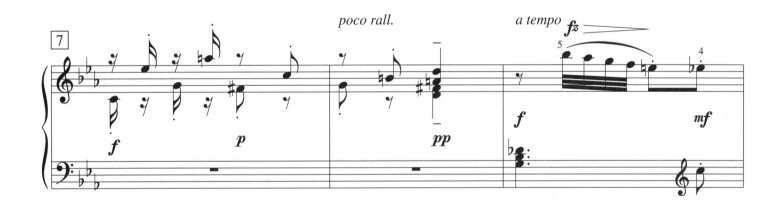

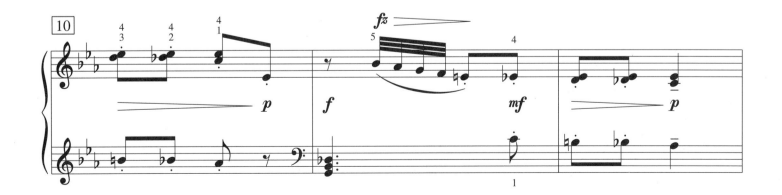

Source: *Six Humorous Bagatelles*, Op. 11 / *Six bagatelles humouristiques, op. 11*

GRADE 5

STUDY NO. 16 / ÉTUDE Nᵒ 16

Marko Tajčević
(1900 - 1984)

Allegretto scherzando ♩ = 132 - 144

Source: *Zwei Stücke aus Lieder von der Mur-Insel,* No. 1

STUDY NO. 1 / ÉTUDE N° 1

Game of Patience / Jeu de réussite, Op. 25, No. 2

GRADE 6

Génari Karganov
(1858 - 1890)

Patience is the name of a card game. / La réussite est le nom d'un jeu de cartes.

Source: *Jugend-album,* Op. 25

STUDY NO. 2 / ÉTUDE Nº 2
Op. 65, No. 13

GRADE 6

Albert Loeschhorn
(1819 - 1905)

Allegro moderato ♩ = 80 - 92

Source: *Etüden für Anfänger*, Op. 65

STUDY NO. 3 / ÉTUDE Nº 3
Op. 55, No. 21

GRADE 6

Theodor Fürchtegott Kirchner
(1823 - 1903)

Source: *Neue Kinderszenen*, Op. 55 (1881)

STUDY NO. 4 / ÉTUDE N° 4
Solfeggio in D Major / Solfège en ré majeur

GRADE 6

Johann Christoph Friedrich Bach
(1732 - 1795)

All dynamics are editorial. / Toutes les indications des nuances sont de la part des rédacteurs.
Source: *Musikalische Nebenstunden* (1787-1788)

STUDY NO. 5 / ÉTUDE N° 6
Heartache / Coeur gros, Op. 32, No. 2

GRADE 6

Robert Fuchs
(1847 - 1927)

Original title / Titre original: "Herzeleid"
Original marking / Indication originale: Ruhig, empfindungsvoll
Source: *Jugendklänge,* Op. 32

STUDY NO. 6 / ÉTUDE N° 6
Farewell / L'adieu, Op. 100, No. 12

GRADE 6

Johann Friedrich Burgmüller
(1806 - 1874)

Source: *25 Études faciles et progressives*, op. 100 / *25 Easy Progressive Studies*, Op. 100

STUDY NO. 7 / ÉTUDE Nº 7
Op. 125, No. 10

Stephen Heller
(1813 - 1888)

GRADE 6

Allegretto ♩. = 50 - 56

Source: *24 Études d'expression et de rythme, op. 125 / 24 Studies for Expression and Rhythm, Op. 125*

STUDY NO. 8 / ÉTUDE Nº 8

Saraband / Sarabande

GRADE 6

John Alcock
(1715 - 1806)

All dynamics and the small notes in m. 24 are editorial. / Toutes les indications des nuances et les petites notes au m. 24 sont de la part des rédacteurs.

Arpeggiate the final chord. / Arpéger le dernier accord.

Source: Suite No. 5 in E minor from *Six Suites of Easy Lessons* (1741)

STUDY NO. 9 / ÉTUDE Nº 9
Miniature
Op. 62, No. 6

GRADE 6

Theodor Fürchtegott Kirchner
(1823 - 1903)

Source: *Miniatüren, 15 leichte Stücke*, Op. 62

STUDY NO. 10 / ÉTUDE N° 10
Horse Ride / Promenade à cheval

GRADE 6

Talivaldis Kenins
(1919 -   )

Source: *Meet Canadian Composers at the Piano*

STUDY NO. 11 / ÉTUDE Nº 11
A Little Song / Une petite chanson
Op. 47, No. 4

GRADE 6

Robert Fuchs
(1847 - 1927)

Original title / Titre original: "Liedchen"
Original marking / Indication originale: Langsam, gesangvoll
Source: *Jugend-Album,* Op. 47 (1890)

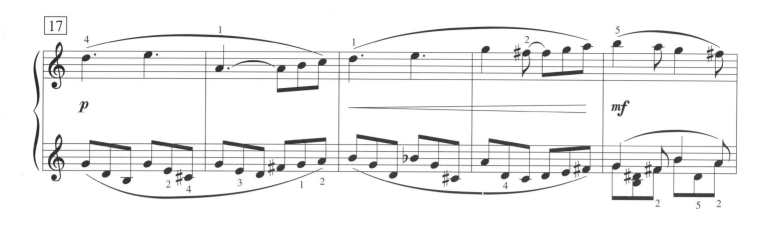

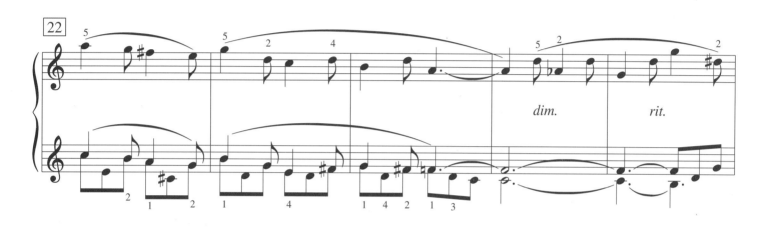

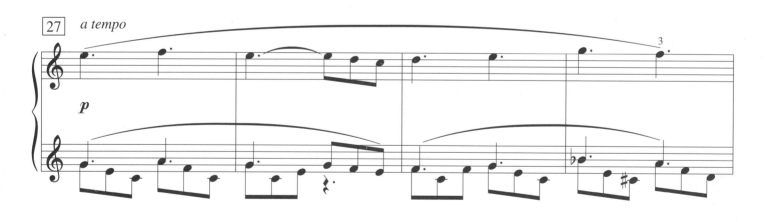

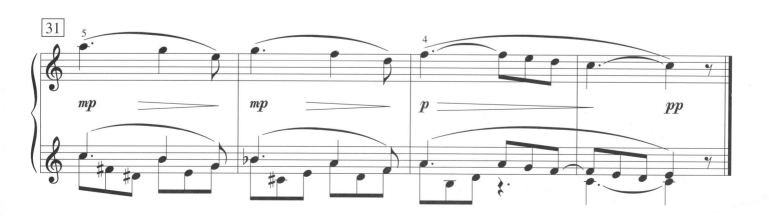

STUDY NO. 12 / ÉTUDE N° 12

GRADE 6

Pál Kadosa
(1903 - 1983)

Source: *55 Small Piano Pieces,* Book 1, No. 49 / *55 Petits morceaux pour piano,* livre 1, n° 49

© Copyright 1960 Editio Musica Budapest. Used by permission.

STUDY NO. 13 / ÉTUDE Nº 13

GRADE 6

Pál Kadosa
(1903 - 1983)

Source: *55 Small Piano Pieces,* Book 1, No. 16 / *55 Petits morceaux pour piano,* livre 1, nº 16
© Copyright 1960 Editio Musica Budapest. Used by permission.

STUDY NO. 14 / ÉTUDE N° 14
Little Willy and the Wind / Petit Willi et le vent, Op. 46, No. 8

GRADE 6

Walter Niemann
(1876 - 1953)

Cheerful / Gai *with a lively step / avec vivacité*

♩ = 112 - 120

Original title / Titre original: "Klein Willy und der Wind"; Original marking / Indication originale: Fröhlich
Source: *In Children's Land,* Op. 46 / *Au pays des enfants,* op. 46